Dad was painting the door. Mum
went out.

Wilf and Wilma came to play.

"Come in," said Dad.

Three children came to the house.
They came to play with Biff.

"Come in," said Biff.

Four children came to the house.
They came to play with Chip.

"Come in," said Chip.

Five children came to play. They
wanted to play with Kipper.

"Come in," said Kipper.

Mum came home.

"What a lot of children! What a
mess!" she said.

Mum looked for Biff, Chip and
Kipper. They were watching
television.

Mum was cross.

Mum gave the children some
biscuits.

They all went home.

Mum went outside.
"Oh no!" said Mum.